DISNEY · PIXAR
FINDING NEMO

Adapted by Steve Heinrich
Illustrated by the Disney Storybook Artists

Nemo is lost, and his father Marlin needs to find him. Read along with me as we go on an exciting adventure. You will know it is time to turn the page when you hear this sound.... Just follow along, and enjoy this wonderful tale about Nemo and Marlin.

publications international, ltd.

Story Reader™

"First day of school!" yells Nemo as he bounces on his sleeping dad, Marlin. Nemo is excited. But Marlin, who worries about everything, is worried. He's very concerned about Nemo's lucky fin. It's smaller than the other one, and it makes him an awkward swimmer.

At school Nemo and his new friends sneak off and see a boat in the distance. Marlin arrives and scolds his son, thinking he was about to swim out to the boat. While Marlin is not looking, Nemo swims all the way to the boat to prove he is brave. A diver from the boat captures Nemo.

Marlin chases the boat until he can't see it anymore.

"Did anybody see a boat?" he yells. Suddenly he runs headfirst into a blue tang fish. Her name is Dory, and she says that she knows which way the boat went. "Thank you!" says Marlin, and off they go to catch the boat.

Soon Dory, who forgets everything, has forgotten why Marlin is following her. Marlin explains about Nemo again, but before they can start back on the path, a giant shark named Bruce shows up.

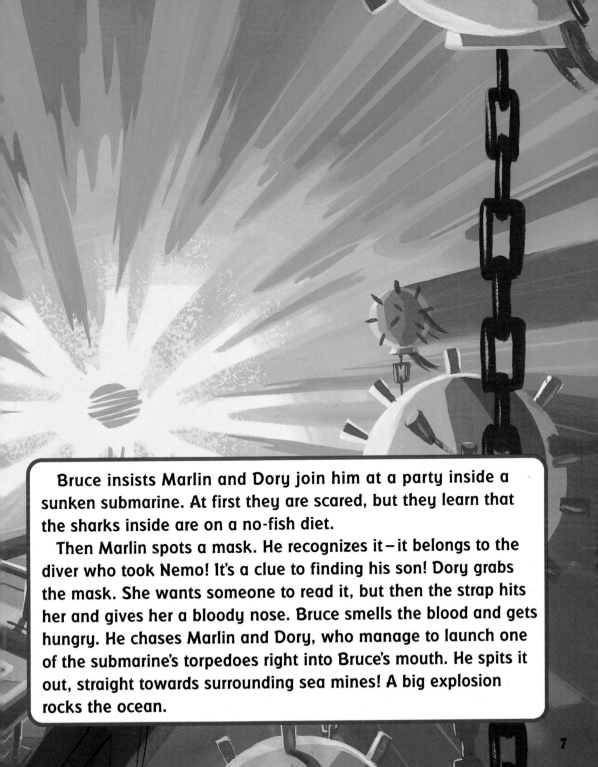

Bruce insists Marlin and Dory join him at a party inside a sunken submarine. At first they are scared, but they learn that the sharks inside are on a no-fish diet.

Then Marlin spots a mask. He recognizes it – it belongs to the diver who took Nemo! It's a clue to finding his son! Dory grabs the mask. She wants someone to read it, but then the strap hits her and gives her a bloody nose. Bruce smells the blood and gets hungry. He chases Marlin and Dory, who manage to launch one of the submarine's torpedoes right into Bruce's mouth. He spits it out, straight towards surrounding sea mines! A big explosion rocks the ocean.

8

The diver, a dentist named Dr. Sherman, takes Nemo to his office and drops him into his fish tank. The other fish in the tank all welcome Nemo. A pelican named Nigel also drops by the office window to welcome Nemo to his new home.

But they soon discover that it won't be Nemo's home for long. The dentist plans to give Nemo away to his little niece, Darla. Darla likes to hold fish in a bag and shake them silly.

Back in the ocean, Dory accidentally drops the mask! She and Marlin swim down into the dark water to find it. They see a light, but this light is attached to a hungry anglerfish.

"Look out!" yells Marlin. As they try to escape, Dory remembers she can read! She uses the light to read the words on the mask: "P. Sherman, 42 Wallaby Way, Sydney."

When they are safe, Dory asks a group of moonfish for directions to Sydney. The moonfish form an arrow to point the way. But they warn Dory that when she and Marlin come to a trench, they need to swim through it, not over it.

Marlin and Dory reach the trench. But already Dory has forgotten the warning. Marlin convinces Dory to swim over the trench because he thinks it will be safer. Within seconds they are surrounded by dangerous jellyfish.

They try to bounce off the tops of the jellyfish to escape, but Dory gets stung just before she reaches clear water. Marlin manages to pull Dory to safety, but he gets stung, too, and passes out.

In the tank a fish named Gill has a plan. Gill came from the ocean, just like Nemo. He wants them all to escape. Gill's plan is to have little Nemo swim into the tank's filter and stop it with a pebble. This will make the tank dirty. When Dr. Sherman cleans it, he'll put each fish in a plastic bag. Then they can roll their plastic bags out the window and into the harbor.

Nemo tries it. But while he's in the filter, the pebble gets loose and Nemo gets sucked towards the moving blades! Gill and the other fish rescue Nemo just in time.

"Dude! Focus, dude!" says a sea turtle to Marlin. Marlin wakes up and realizes he and Dory were rescued by a group of sea turtles swimming on the East Australian Current, which is headed straight for Sydney. Dory is playing hide-and-seek with the kid turtles. The sea turtles want to hear about Marlin's adventure. "This is going to be good, I can tell," Dory says as Marlin begins his tale.

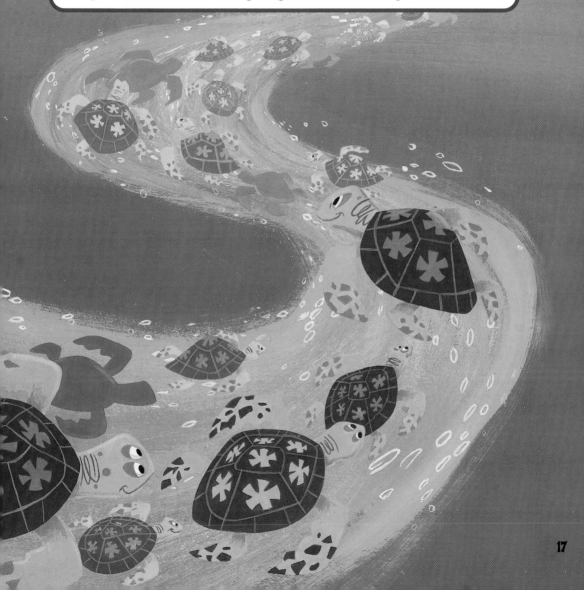

Marlin and Dory leave the turtles when they get near Sydney. Dory sees a whale and asks it for directions. But the whale sucks them into his mouth!

Dory tries to talk to the whale. Marlin is worried. Dory can't speak "Whale," he thinks. She's going to make the whale upset.

"He says to move to the back of the throat," says Dory. "Everything's going to be all right." Marlin puts his faith in Dory, lets go of the whale's tongue, and falls to the back of the throat. They both go shooting out the whale's blowhole high into the air!

Soon the turtles have spread Marlin's story throughout the ocean. When Nigel hears it, he goes to tell Nemo. Nemo is so excited, he tries the pebble plan again, and it works!

Dr. Sherman sees the slimy fish tank. But instead of cleaning out the tank, he buys a special filter that cleans the tank for him. Then Dr. Sherman grabs only one plastic bag. It is for Nemo. Darla is on her way. But Nemo has a new plan. He will play dead! He hopes to be flushed down the toilet. Gill says that all drains lead to the ocean.

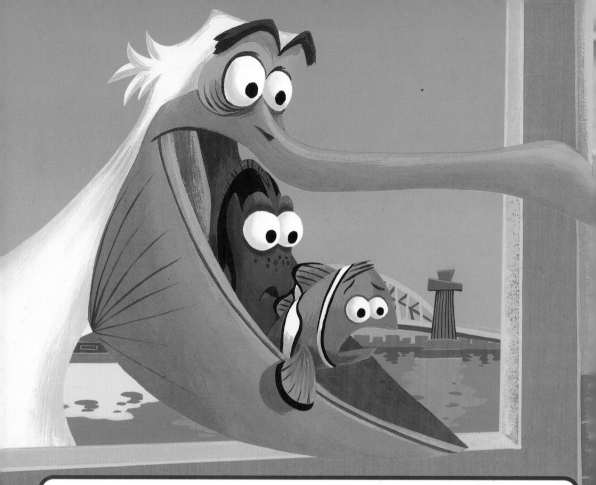

Darla arrives, and Nemo plays dead. But the dentist heads for the trash can, not the toilet. At that moment Nigel tumbles into the office. He found Marlin and Dory, and rushed them to the office in his beak! Surprised, the dentist loses control of Nemo's bag. It flies through the air and lands on the dental tray in front of Darla. Marlin sees Nemo and thinks he really is dead.

"Fishy! Wake up!" Darla yells as she shakes Nemo's bag. To save Nemo, Gill shoots from the tank's volcano and lands on Darla's head. She drops Nemo's bag, breaking it. Gill lands on a dentist's tool and launches Nemo into the sink and down the drain. Nemo has escaped!

Nigel drops Marlin and Dory back into the ocean. Marlin, thinking he has lost Nemo, heads home without Dory.

Nemo escapes from the drainpipe into the ocean and finds a sad fish. It's Dory! But she has no idea who he is. She has already forgotten. But when Dory sees the word "Sydney" on a pipe, she remembers everything. Together, she and Nemo find Marlin.

Marlin, Nemo, and Dory go back home to tell everyone about their adventures. Nemo has been found!